POWER BASICS +PLUS

Introduction to Composition

Test Pack

WALCH PUBLISHING

Certified Chain of Custody
Promoting Sustainable
Forest Management
www.sfiprogram.org

SGS-SFI/COC-US09/5501

1   2   3   4   5   6   7   8   9   10

ISBN 0-8251-5756-0

Copyright © 2005

J. Weston Walch, Publisher

P. O. Box 658 • Portland, Maine 04104-0658

walch.com

Printed in the United States of America

WALCH PUBLISHING

Table of Contents

To the Teacher

Power Basics® is a complete textbook program designed to meet the needs of students who are daunted by traditional textbooks. *Power Basics* was created with the teacher in mind, as well. The test pack for each student text in the *Power Basics* program includes straightforward, accurate, and easy-to-score assessment tools.

Each test pack includes

- a pretest that covers all the material in the student text

- a comprehensive test for every unit of the student text

- a posttest for final testing and assessment after working through the entire student text

- an answer key and testing guidance for both teacher and student

With testing a critical component of a school's curriculum today, students need to learn test-taking skills. This *Power Basics* test pack provides not only tests related to the student text, but special reference sections devoted to the topic of testing. "Testing Students Who Do Not Test Well" helps you give all your students the tools they need to be successful test-takers. "Test-Taking Strategies for *Power Basics*" and "Strategies for Standardized Testing" give students useful information about preparing for the tests in this test pack and for high-stakes standardized tests. These sections include key strategies for approaching tests with confidence. You may want to distribute and discuss these test-preparation tools before the pretest.

Finally, a handy record-keeping form permits you to track your students' progress as they work through the *Power Basics* student text.

Everything you need for test success is right here in *Power Basics*!

Testing Students Who Do Not Test Well

There are many reasons why some students do not test well. There may be language barriers, learning differences, or a failure to perceive the relevance or importance of a given assessment.

When working with a group of students who do not test well, it is important to identify the causes for the problems and, when possible, to find individual solutions for particular students.

Students who are easily distracted or who have been diagnosed with ADD or ADHD may benefit from taking the test in a quieter, more restrictive atmosphere. Give such students the option of taking a test during a break period, such as a study hall or lunch period. If possible, provide study carrels in your classroom to minimize external distractions.

Students with a low level of English proficiency will benefit from either having the instructions translated into their native language, having translation materials on their desks during the test, or having a translator present. Such students will invariably need more time than others to complete a test.

For students who see no benefit to a given test, discuss the purposes and benefits of testing in general with them ahead of time. There will be tests in every area of the student's life, from taking the test to become a licensed driver to getting into the college or trade school of his or her choice. Test-taking is an important skill, one that will serve students well throughout life.

The work you do with your students on test preparation will provide them with the tools they need to master not only the tests in this course, but the tests they will face throughout their educational experiences and careers.

Test-Taking Strategies for *Power Basics*®

Tests are a part of life. Whether you're facing a test in the classroom, a standardized test, or even a driver's test, there are tools you can use to help you be successful. The best way to do well on a test is to pay attention in class and study the material. But you can also prepare in other ways. Knowing how the test is set up can help you approach the test with confidence.

Tests come in many formats. They will vary in their structure. Some tests may contain only one question format, such as multiple choice. Others may have true/false, matching, fill-in-the-blank, short-answer, or essay questions. Some tests may ask you to read a passage and then answer questions about it. Others may ask you to refer to or make a graph or a chart. No matter what types of questions the test contains, using specific strategies for each question type can help you be successful.

The tests for the *Power Basics*® program may include multiple-choice, short-answer, or essay questions. The following strategies can help you answer these types of questions.

Multiple Choice

In multiple-choice questions, you read each question and choose the best answer out of two or more choices. These choices are usually labeled with the letters *a, b, c, d,* and *e,* depending on the number of choices. Use the following steps to help you answer multiple-choice questions.

- Read the directions very carefully. Some multiple-choice tests will ask you to select the *correct* answer, and others will ask you to select the *best* answer.

- Read the first part of the question very carefully. Look for negative words such as *not, never, except, unless,* and so forth.

- Answer each question in your mind before looking at the answer choices. Then read the answer choices before selecting an answer.

- After reading the choices, rule out the choices that are obviously incorrect. Then choose an answer from the remaining choices.

Test-Taking Strategies
for *Power Basics,* continued

Short Answer

Short-answer questions require answers that vary in length. Some may call for an answer that is a sentence or two in length. Others may need a paragraph or two to be answered completely. You'll know how long your answer should be based on the question and sometimes on the amount of space you're given to write the answer. Use the following steps to help you answer short-answer questions.

- If the response requires one or two sentences, be clear, direct, and specific.

- If the response requires a paragraph or more, begin with a strong topic sentence that states your main idea.

- If you're responding to a passage, be sure to refer clearly to the information in the passage.

- Use specific examples or quotations from the passage if the question asks you to do so.

Essay

Essay-length responses require you to use several paragraphs to explore a topic. An often-used essay format is five paragraphs: an introduction, three paragraphs that each discuss the main idea with supporting examples, and a conclusion. Use the following steps to help you answer essay questions.

- Read the question several times. Make sure you clearly understand what you are being asked to write.

- Think about the question and what you might want to include in your answer. Make a list of all the details you remember about the topic.

- Select your main points, and put the information together in a brief outline.

- Make sure you have a strong topic sentence that states the main idea.

- Include any additional information you need to make your answer clear.

INTRODUCTION TO COMPOSITION • PRETEST

Read each group of words. If the words form a complete sentence, circle *a*. If they do not, circle *b*.

1. The gurgling brook rushed over the rocks.
   - **a.** complete sentence
   - **b.** fragment

2. Tammy seems to read at the speed of light.
   - **a.** complete sentence
   - **b.** fragment

3. Rushing up and down the halls and around the furniture.
   - **a.** complete sentence
   - **b.** fragment

Underline the simple subject in each sentence.

4. Maxine and Vivian wrote to their grandmother.

5. The Johnson twins both like to play softball.

6. Through the dark woods trudged the two hikers.

Underline the simple predicate in each sentence.

7. The squirrel dashed up the oak tree.

8. The children slid down the snowy hill on trash can lids.

9. After the game, the boys bought lunch.

Read the sentences below. Decide what type of sentence each is. Circle the letter of the correct answer.

10. Ms. Millard lives next door to Mr. Ali.

    a. simple

    b. compound

    c. complex

11. The Donners drove to Manchester, and then they flew to Quebec.

    a. simple

    b. compound

    c. complex

12. Although it is beautiful, Montreal is very cold in the winter.

    a. simple

    b. compound

    c. complex

The following sentences have problems with sentence structure. On the lines, rewrite each sentence so that it is clear and correct.

13. Morgan and Chas had to get up early their flight left at seven in the morning.

_____

_____

14. They did not have much time to say good-bye, they had to pack.

_____

_____

15. Morgan's favorite activities during her visit were visiting the art museum, watching the skaters on the pond, and to tour the harbor.

_____

_____

16. Chas liked the science museum, the walking tour, and seeing the ballet.

_____

_____

17. She loaded the bags into the car waving to us.

_____

_____

Read the paragraph. Then answer the questions.

Marisa thinks she would like to be a fashion designer someday. To reach that goal, she is taking a variety of courses in school. First, she has taken many art classes, including drawing. These classes help her develop her creative talent. She has also studied marketing. This will serve her well when she starts her own company. Marketing is a fun class. Finally, she is taking practical business courses, such as keyboarding and bookkeeping. Marisa knows that she may start her career as a support person in someone else's business. She wants to have the skills necessary to grab an opportunity when it knocks!

18. What is the topic sentence of the paragraph?

　　a. Marisa thinks she would like to be a fashion designer someday.

　　b. To reach that goal, she is taking a variety of courses in school.

　　c. She wants to have the skills necessary to grab an opportunity when it knocks!

19. Which sentence is not relevant to the paragraph?

　　a. These classes help her develop her creative talent.

　　b. She has also studied marketing.

　　c. Marketing is a fun class.

20. Which sentence could be a substitute concluding sentence for the paragraph?

　　a. Marisa likes fashion design.

　　b. Marisa has the drive to do what it takes to fulfill her dream.

　　c. It is important to choose a career with good job opportunities.

Read the following paragraph. It is the introductory paragraph of an essay. Then answer the questions.

> People concerned about health often avoid chocolate as a high-calorie, fat-heavy food. Those beliefs may be valid about regular chocolate bars, but chocolate in other forms may have health benefits. Some studies suggest that chemicals in cocoa may improve heart health, increase blood flow, and prevent some cancers. This is good news for chocolate-lovers and people who want to eat healthily.

21. What is the topic sentence for the essay?

   a. People concerned about health often avoid chocolate as a high-calorie, fat-heavy food.

   b. Those beliefs may be valid about regular chocolate bars, but chocolate in other forms may have health benefits.

   c. This is good news for chocolate-lovers and people who want to eat healthily.

22. What points would you expect to read in the supporting paragraphs of this essay?

   a. people's concerns about health

   b. recipes for chocolate-lovers

   c. the ways cocoa can improve health

Circle the letter of the correct answer.

23. What order do you follow in writing an essay?

   a. create an outline, focus your topic, brainstorm

   b. brainstorm, focus your topic, create an outline

   c. brainstorm, create an outline, focus your topic

Follow the directions to edit the paragraph.

24. Use proofreaders' marks to mark corrections in the paragraph.

> Nicola and Matthew was waiting for Ms. Oliveira to post the cast list. They have both tried out last week for the role of narrator in the school musical. Since it did not mater whether the narrator was a boy or a girl, they both had hope. Being nervous and excitement was making both of them jumpy.

25. Rewrite the paragraph from item 24, making the corrections you marked.

_____

_____

_____

_____

_____

_____

_____

_____

_____

UNIT 1 TEST • SENTENCES

Read the sentence below. Then answer the questions.

Maria and Shonda ate lunch together yesterday.

1. What is the complete subject of the sentence?
   a. Maria and Shonda
   b. ate lunch
   c. together yesterday

2. What is the simple subject of the sentence?
   a. Maria, Shonda
   b. ate
   c. lunch

3. What is the complete predicate of the sentence?
   a. Maria and Shonda ate
   b. ate lunch together yesterday
   c. together, yesterday

4. What is the simple predicate of the sentence?
   a. Maria, Shonda
   b. ate
   c. lunch

Read each group of words. Decide if each is a complete sentence or a fragment. Circle the letter of the correct answer.

5. After the band played the final song of the concert.
   a. complete sentence
   b. fragment

6. The fans shouted for one more tune.

    a. complete sentence

    b. fragment

7. The man with the dark blue suit and the striped coat.

    a. complete sentence

    b. fragment

8. Snow covered the sidewalk.

    a. complete sentence

    b. fragment

9. The puddle froze solid during the night.

    a. complete sentence

    b. fragment

Read each sentence. Decide if each is a simple sentence, a compound sentence, or a complex sentence. Circle the letter of the correct answer.

10. Hannah and Jacob laughed and played at the park.

    a. simple

    b. compound

    c. complex

11. Maura ran until her sides hurt.

    a. simple

    b. compound

    c. complex

12. Mr. Hadley called for quiet, but the students did not hear him.

    a. simple

    b. compound

    c. complex

13. Cameron rode to the mall.

   a. simple

   b. compound

   c. complex

14. Donell finished his social studies essay.

   a. simple

   b. compound

   c. complex

15. Walter threw the ball, and the dog chased it down the hill.

   a. simple

   b. compound

   c. complex

Read each group of words. If the group is a correct sentence, circle *a*. If it is a run-on sentence, circle *b*. If it is a comma splice, circle *c*.

16. The boys wanted to camp in a tent their dad preferred to sleep in a cabin.

   a. correct sentence

   b. run-on sentence

   c. comma splice

17. Michael did not buy the shoes, they cost too much.

   a. correct sentence

   b. run-on sentence

   c. comma splice

18. The rival teams faced each other on the court.

   a. correct sentence

   b. run-on sentence

   c. comma splice

19. Andre turned his seat he could not see the board.

    a. correct sentence

    b. run-on sentence

    c. comma splice

The following sentences do not have parallel structure. Rewrite each sentence so that it does have parallel structure.

20. Parva looked under the bed, in the closet, and the drawer.

_____

_____

21. Dana likes to bake cookies more than eating them.

_____

_____

22. Basketball, track, and playing football are my favorite sports.

_____

_____

Read each sentence. If the sentence is clear, write *clear* on the line. If the sentence has a poorly placed modifier, rewrite the sentence so that it is clear.

23. Swollen from the rain, the river flowed over its banks.

_____

24. Snapping in the wind, I watched the thin branches.

_____

25. I enjoyed the sunset shielding my eyes.

_____

UNIT 2 TEST • PARAGRAPHS

Read the sentences. Circle the letter of the sentence in each group that would make the most focused, clear topic sentence for a paragraph.

1. **a.** Several new technologies make keeping in touch with people easier than before.

    b. E-mail is fun.

    c. Few people use "snail mail" to keep in touch these days.

    d. "Snail mail" is frustrating because it is slow.

2. **a.** Cats are better than dogs.

    b. Cats make ideal pets for busy people for several reasons.

    c. The Himalayan is an attractive and friendly longhaired cat.

    d. My friend has a friendly cat.

3. **a.** Homemade bread smells wonderful.

    b. There are several good reasons to bake your own bread.

    c. Bread bought in a store contains preservatives.

    d. Homemade bread has fresher ingredients than store-bought bread.

The paragraph below does not have a topic sentence. Read the paragraph. Then circle the letter of the best topic sentence for the paragraph.

Ms. Martino was fair and consistent. She let you know the rules at the beginning of the year. If you followed them, all was well. If not, you knew what the consequences would be. Ms. Martino did not play favorites, and she did not bend her rules except in extreme cases. She was willing to listen to an excuse, but she was not easily convinced that a reason was valid. I think Ms. Martino was an admirable teacher.

4. **a.** Ms. Martino was a tough grader.

    b. I respected Ms. Martino.

    c. Ms. Martino was well-liked.

    d. Ms. Martino was in her forties.

Read the paragraphs. Then answer the questions that follow each.

Several types of rodents make excellent pets and do not require a lot of time, space, or expense. Gerbils, for example, are active and fun to watch. Hamsters, too, are popular rodent pets. They live about as long as gerbils, two to three years, but they are solitary. You need to keep only one hamster. Mice, which live one to three years, are active and playful. They are social and do well in pairs or small groups. Guinea pigs can live five to seven years, and, because of their gentleness, they are a popular choice for families. If you are too busy to meet the needs of a cat or a dog, consider a rodent pet.

5. Which is the topic sentence of the paragraph?

   a. Several types of rodents make excellent pets and do not require a lot of time, space, or expense.

   b. Mice, which live one to three years, are active and playful.

   c. Guinea pigs can live five to seven years, and, because of their gentleness, they are a popular choice for families.

   d. Gerbils, for example, are active and fun to watch.

6. Which of these could be a substitute for the concluding sentence?

   a. Guinea pigs are satisfying pets to own.

   b. Rodents do not need as much care as cats or dogs.

   c. Any of these rodents is a good choice of pet for busy people.

   d. Beavers, squirrels, and woodchucks are also rodents.

7. What type of paragraph is this?

   a. cause-and-effect paragraph

   b. list paragraph

   c. narrative paragraph

Marcus had decided to buy a new used car. He loved his old Mustang, but it had broken down several times in the last month. The repair bills totaled several hundred dollars. Besides maintenance, gas was expensive. The Mustang did not get great gas mileage. What made Marcus's decision possible was his birthday. His aunt knew he depended on his car, and she had sent him a generous check as a gift. Marcus was ready to start researching cars!

8. What is the topic sentence of this paragraph?

    a. Marcus had decided to buy a new used car.

    b. The repair bills totaled several hundred dollars.

    c. What made Marcus's decision possible was his birthday.

9. Which of these could be a substitute for the concluding sentence?

    a. Marcus loved to drive.

    b. The Mustang was a great model, but Marcus preferred something newer.

    c. These things came together to nudge Marcus to finally buy another car.

10. What type of paragraph is this?

    a. cause-and-effect paragraph

    b. list paragraph

    c. narrative paragraph

Read the topic sentences. Then read the possible supporting sentences. Circle the letter of the supporting sentence that is not relevant.

11. Besides helping parents, day care provides benefits to children as well.

    a. Children make friends their own age in day care settings.

    b. Day care centers offer educational experiences.

    c. Some day care centers are in private homes.

12. Homemade gifts are special.

    a. Homemade gifts are less expensive than bought gifts.

    b. Gifts made by hand show that the giver thinks the receiver is worth the effort.

    c. A custom-made gift is unique; no one else will have exactly the same thing.

13. Winter is my favorite season.

    a. I enjoy ice skating and sledding.

    b. I love cold-weather clothes: fun mittens, chunky scarves, stocking hats.

    c. Fall is not much fun.

14. I prefer sweaters made of cotton to those made of wool.

     a. Cotton is easy to care for.

     b. Wool can be scratchy.

     c. My favorite cotton sweater is blue.

The following paragraph does not have a concluding sentence. Read the paragraph. Then circle the letter of the best concluding sentence.

A toasted cheese sandwich makes a quick, easy meal when you do not have time for something fancier. It provides protein and calcium, and it tastes great! Toasting the sandwich makes it a little more than a snack.

15.   **a.** Toasted cheese is my favorite sandwich.

     b. When time is short, a toasted cheese sandwich is a satisfying meal.

     c. Cheese is a healthy food.

     d. There are many varieties of cheese you can use.

UNIT 3 TEST • ESSAYS

Read the following introductory paragraph for an essay. Then circle the letter of the answer to each question.

Do you know how good for you regular exercise is? There are many benefits! Exercise can help your heart, boost your mood, and give you an activity to share with others. All these plusses make physical activity worthwhile.

1. How does the author capture your attention?
    a. by asking a question
    b. by making a shocking statement
    c. by using a specific example

2. Which is the topic sentence of the essay?
    a. There are many benefits!
    b. It can help your heart, boost your mood, and give you an activity to share with others.
    c. All these plusses make exercise worthwhile.

3. Which of the following is likely to be a supporting point in the essay?
    a. ways exercise increases heart health
    b. expenses of different sports
    c. the benefits of joining a gym

4. Which of the following is the best concluding paragraph for this essay?
    a. Exercise does take commitment—in time and sometimes in money. The benefits, however, are well worth the investment. Exercise every day—for your health, for your sense of well-being, and for the fun of it!
    b. The heart is a muscle, and like all muscles, it needs to be exercised. The regular stress of exercise strengthens the heart. A strong heart is worth the effort of exercise.
    c. Playing on a team gives you a community as well as a fun activity. You will make friends who share your interests. Team sports are a great pastime.

Read the following introductory paragraph for an essay. Then circle the letter of the answer to each question.

> Unemployment soars at levels not seen in years. Our economy has shifted many jobs to remote locations. This means that jobs once held by local people are now filled less expensively by people in other countries. Studies show that this trend is continuing. There are still, however, some areas of job growth. Recent graduates will have good luck in service industries, such as the trades and health care. These are jobs that require face-to-face or hands-on skills.

5. How does the author get the reader's attention?

  a. by asking a question

  b. by making a shocking statement

  c. by using a specific example

6. What is the topic sentence of the essay?

  a. Unemployment soars at levels not seen in years.

  b. Studies show that this trend is continuing.

  c. There are still, however, some areas of job growth.

7. Which of the following is likely to be a supporting point in the essay?

  a. trends in sending non-service jobs overseas

  b. descriptions of service jobs that are growing

  c. unemployment statistics for non-service jobs

8. Which of the following is the best concluding paragraph for this essay?

  a. Recent graduates need to be aware of the job market. Learning is great, but students should be practical, too. A diploma is not worth much without a paycheck.

  b. The knowledge gained in many general courses can be applied to a variety of jobs. Getting involved in a range of activities outside school also builds an impressive résumé. Students should apply for jobs in fields that relate to their interests.

  c. Preparing for life after school is important. With skills that are in demand and that require a person to be present, graduates will find many job options. Jobs that can be done from a distance are not as secure.

Read the paragraphs. Then answer the question that follows each.

I keep a lot of stuff in my locker. At the top is a shelf. It is tall enough to hold all my books, as long as I keep them stacked. Below that is a space to hang my coat and stow my gym bag. I leave my backpack there when I go to art or music and don't need to carry a lot of books. The floor of my locker is where I stick my sneakers after gym. I also, I admit, toss trash there, such as snack wrappers and stray bits of paper. Hung on the inside of the door is a plastic mirror. I also stuck a postcard there from my friend in Paris. My locker holds everything I need for a busy day at school.

9. How is this paragraph arranged?

   a. chronological order

   b. spatial order

   c. comparison and contrast

Dom had a lot to do and not a lot of time in which to do it. First, he ran home from the bus stop. Next, he hopped in the car and headed to the tux rental shop. From there, Dom sprinted across the street to the florist and paid for the corsage he had ordered. Then he jumped back in the car and drove home. He debated what to do next; it was still a little early to get dressed. He decided to have a snack so that he wouldn't starve later while waiting for the dinner to be served. After loading his dirty plate in the dishwasher, Dom showered. He carefully styled his hair and brushed his teeth. Then he put on the tux, with a little help from Dad to get the tie right. When he was dressed, he went to the car to go pick up his date. Before he got out of the driveway, his mom ran out the door with something in her hand. The corsage!

10. How is this paragraph arranged?

   a. chronological order

   b. spatial order

   c. comparison and contrast

UNIT 4 TEST • THE WRITING PROCESS

Answer the questions in your own words.

1. What are the steps you follow in writing a first draft?

_____

_____

2. List two things an introductory paragraph should do.

_____

_____

3. How many main points should you cover in each supporting paragraph?

_____

4. What does relevance mean in an essay?

_____

_____

Now you will plan and write the first draft of an essay. The general topic is the following: *Our school should (or should not) have vending machines that sell soda and candy.*

5. Use the space below to brainstorm a list of ideas. Then focus your topic.

_____

_____

_____

_____

_____

_____

_____

6. Now create an outline showing your support points and details.

7. Next, write a topic sentence

_____

_____

8. Use the outline to write your introductory paragraph.

_____

_____

_____

_____

_____

_____

_____

_____

9. Using your introductory paragraph and your outline, write your supporting paragraphs.

_____

_____

_____

_____

_____

_____

_____

_____

_____

_____

_____

_____

_____

_____

_____

_____

10. Finally, write a concluding paragraph for your essay.

_____

_____

_____

_____

_____

_____

_____

UNIT 5 TEST • EDITING

Match each proofreaders' mark on the left with its meaning on the right. Write the letter of the correct meaning on the line.

1. || _____   **a.** subject-verb agreement

2. s-v agr _____   **b.** close up; write as one word

3. ^ _____   **c.** insert

4. ⊙ _____   **d.** parallel structure problem

5. sp _____   **e.** sentence fragment

6. frag _____   **f.** spelling error

7. ⌣ _____   **g.** insert a period

The following sentences contain mechanical, grammatical, or structural errors. Mark the corrections with proofreaders' marks. Then rewrite each sentence with the corrections made.

8. The island paardise was ruined by smog.

   _____

   _____

9. "How can that be? Jane asked.

   _____

   _____

10. The bleachers at atkins park are rickety.

   _____

   _____

11. Eli road to school on his bike.

   _____

   _____

12. Annette and Jose has gone to the lake.

   _____

   _____

13. Every student voted for their choice of mascot.

   _____

14. The dogs bone is under that rock.

_____

15. For fun, Jesse likes to write in his journal, read comics, and watches action movies.

_____

16. The following paragraph contains many errors. Mark the corrections with proofreaders' marks. Then rewrite the paragraph with the corrections made.

The final exma was at noon. Glenda felt her hands sweat, her head ache, and her heart pounding. This test was very important. Her score on this one exam would effect her grade. She wanted at least a *B* to keep up her averge. Glenda also wanted a good grade for another reason if she did well her parents would let her spend a week with her friend at a vacation cabin. Glenda has a lot riding on this test. She took a deep breathe to calm her nerves. She reached out a steady hand and open the class room door. She saw her friend across the room Glenda took a seat near her. When the teacher, Mrs. Montagu, called for silence and passed out the tests. Glenda relaxed. She had studied, and she knew the material.

_____

_____

_____

_____

_____

_____

_____

_____

_____

INTRODUCTION TO COMPOSITION • POSTTEST

Read each group of words. If the words form a complete sentence, circle *a*. If they do not, circle *b*.

1. The ground shook.
    a. complete sentence
    b. fragment

2. April showers bring May flowers.
    a. complete sentence
    b. fragment

3. After walking across town and riding the bus to the mall.
    a. complete sentence
    b. fragment

4. The cat, orange and white, with long, drooping whiskers.
    a. complete sentence
    b. fragment

Underline the simple subject in each sentence.

5. Bree, Lauren, and Rachel saw the new movie last weekend.

6. Donna had the flu all week!

7. Mrs. McCann's class read *Huckleberry Finn* this year.

Underline the simple predicate in each sentence.

8. Bree, Lauren, and Rachel saw the new movie last weekend.

9. Donna had the flu all week!

10. Mrs. McCann's class read *Huckleberry Finn* this year.

_____

Read the sentences below. Decide what type of sentence each is. Circle the letter of the correct answer.

11. Organic gardening has become popular.

    a. simple

    b. compound

    c. complex

12. The fruit at that market is good, but the dairy products are not fresh.

    a. simple

    b. compound

    c. complex

13. When I have a lot to do, I write a list.

    a. simple

    b. compound

    c. complex

14. I found my keys and some change in the couch.

    a. simple

    b. compound

    c. complex

The following sentences have problems with sentence structure. On the lines, rewrite each sentence so that it is clear and correct.

15. Running the hundred-yard dash, my nose was red with cold.

_____

_____

16. I saw that woman at the museum with the red skirt.

_____

_____

17. Nina has to study for a test, she also has to do her math homework.

_____

_____

18. Reading, swimming, and baking is some of Neil's favorite activities.

_____

_____

Read the paragraph. Then answer the questions.

> The llama serves many purposes for the Andean Indians. The meat of the llama supplies food. Llama meat is tasty. The animal's hide is made into sandals. Its coat is used to make blankets. Even its droppings provide fuel for fires. The Andean Indians do not waste any part of this valuable animal.

19. What is the topic sentence of this paragraph?

  a. The llama serves many purposes for the Andean Indians.

  b. The animal's hide is made into sandals.

  c. Even its droppings provide fuel for fires.

  d. Its coat is used to make blankets.

20. Which sentence is not relevant to the paragraph?

  a. Even its droppings provide fuel for fires.

  b. Llama meat is tasty.

  c. The meat of the llama supplies food.

  c. The animal's hide is made into sandals.

21. Which sentence could be a substitute concluding sentence for the paragraph?

  a. Llamas are sometimes seen at petting zoos.

  b. Llama hair makes a tough rope.

  c. The Andean Indians depend on the llama to fulfill some basic needs.

  c. Llamas are amazing animals.

Read the following paragraph. It is the introductory paragraph of an essay. Then answer the questions.

> Fellow hikers, are you ready to hit the trail yet? No? You still need to hoist your heavy bedroll and backpack onto your shoulders? You have to help your buddy arrange the tent on his back? Whew! Maybe you should think about inviting a llama on your next camping trip. The llama is becoming a popular pack animal. It is friendly to the environment, it is easy to feed and does not require much water, and it can keep away certain undesirable animals from a campsite.

22. What is the topic sentence for the essay?
    a. Fellow hikers, are you ready to hit the trail yet?
    b. The llama is becoming a popular pack animal.
    c. You have to help your buddy arrange the tent on his back?
    d. You still need to hoist your heavy bedroll and backpack onto your shoulders?

23. What points do you expect to read about in supporting paragraphs of this essay?
    a. reasons people take llamas as pack animals on camping trips
    b. how to select and care for a llama
    c. places to hike with a llama
    d. the cost of keeping a llama

24. Use proofreaders' marks to mark corrections in the paragraph.

> Margo's plan worked with out a hitch. Yelena would never guess that her friends were planning a surprize party for her, her birthday was not for three weeks. Last week, Margo and erik called Yelena's sister to find out whom to invite. Then they bought invitations, filled them out, stamp them, and put them in the mail. Everyone have said they would come. Now Erik just has to get Yelena to Margo's house. He told the birthday girl that Margo needs help studying.

25. Rewrite the paragraph from item 24, making the corrections you marked.

_____

_____

_____

_____

_____

_____

_____

_____

_____

_____

_____

Answer Key

Pretest

1. a
2. a
3. b
4. <u>Maxine</u> and <u>Vivian</u> wrote to their grandmother.
5. The Johnson <u>twins</u> both like to play softball.
6. Through the dark woods trudged the two <u>hikers</u>.
7. The squirrel <u>dashed</u> up the oak tree.
8. The children <u>slid</u> down the snowy hill on trash can lids.
9. After the game, the boys <u>bought</u> lunch.
10. a
11. b
12. c
13. Answers will vary. The following are sample answers: Morgan and Chas had to get up early; their flight left at seven in the morning. OR Morgan and Chas had to get up early. Their flight left at seven in the morning. OR Morgan and Chas had to get up early, since their flight left at seven in the morning.
14. Answers will vary. The following are sample answers: They did not have much time to say good-bye; they had to pack. OR They did not have much time to say good-bye. They had to pack. OR Because they had to pack, they did not have much time to say good-bye.
15. Morgan's favorite activities during her visit were visiting the art museum, watching the skaters on the pond, and touring the harbor.
16. Answers will vary. The following are sample answers: Chas liked the science museum, the walking tour, and the ballet. OR Chas liked visiting the science museum, taking the walking tour, and seeing the ballet.
17. Waving to us, she loaded the bags into the car.
18. b
19. c
20. b
21. b
22. c
23. b
24. There are five errors. Some corrections may vary. The following are sample answers:

s-vagr Nicola and Matthew ~~was~~ **were** waiting for Ms. Oliveira to post the cast list. They

s-vagr ~~have~~ **had** both tried out last week for the role of narrator in the school musical.

sp Since it did not (mater) **t** whether the narrator was a boy or a girl, they both

|| had hope. ~~Being~~ nervous **ness** and

s-vagr excitement ~~was~~ **were** making both of them jumpy.

25. Nicola and Matthew were waiting for Ms. Oliveira to post the cast list. They had both tried out last week for the role of narrator in the school musical. Since it did not matter whether the narrator was a boy or a girl, they both had hope. Nervousness and excitement were making both of them jumpy.

Unit 1 Test: Sentences

1. a
2. a
3. b
4. b
5. b
6. a
7. b
8. a
9. a
10. a
11. c
12. b
13. a
14. a
15. b
16. b
17. c
18. a
19. b
20. Parva looked under the bed, in the closet, and in the drawer.
21. Dana likes baking cookies more than eating them. OR Dana likes to bake cookies more than to eat them.
22. Basketball, track, and football are my favorite sports.

23. clear
24. I watched the thin branches snapping in the wind.
25 Shielding my eyes, I enjoyed the sunset.

Unit 2 Test: Paragraphs

1. a
2. b
3. b
4. b
5. a
6. c
7. b
8. a
9. c
10. a
11. c
12. a
13. c
14. c
15. b

Unit 3 Test: Essays

1. a
2. a
3. a
4. a
5. b
6. c
7. b
8. c
9. b
10. a

Unit 4 Test: The Writing Process

Answers will vary. The following are sample answers.

1. First, you brainstorm about the topic and make a list. Then you look at your list to focus on one narrowed topic. Next, you organize your information in an outline. Using the outline, you write a topic sentence and then the rest of the first draft.
2. An introductory paragraph should tell the topic of the essay, catch the reader's attention, and preview the main points of the essay.
3. one
4. Relevance means that every supporting point is related to the topic and does not contain extra information.

5.–10. Answers will vary.

Unit 5 Test: Editing

1. d
2. a
3. c
4. g
5. f
6. e
7. b

8. The island pa*rad*ise was ruined by smog.   tr
The island paradise was ruined by smog.

9. "How can that be? Jane" asked.
"How can that be?" Jane asked.

10. The bleachers at atkins park are rickety.
The bleachers at Atkins Park are rickety.

11. Eli ~~road~~ *rode* to school on his bike.   sp
Eli rode to school on his bike.

12. Annette and Josie ~~has~~ *have* gone to the lake.   s-v agr
Annette and Josie have gone to the lake.

13. Every student voted for ~~their~~ *his or her* choice of mascot.   ref
Every student voted for his or her choice of mascot.

14. The dog's bone is under that rock.
The dog's bone is under that rock.

15. For fun, Jesse likes to write in his journal, read comics, and watches action movies. ||

For fun, Jesse likes to write in his journal, read comics, and watch action movies. OR For fun, Jesse writes in his journal, reads comics, and watches action movies.

16. There are ten errors. Some corrections may vary. The following are sample answers:

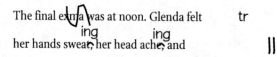

The final ex*tra* was at noon. Glenda felt   tr
her hands sweat*ing*, her head ach*ing*, and ||
her heart pounding. This test was very important. Her
score on this one exam
would effect→*affect* her grade. She wanted at
least a *B* to keep up her *a*verge. Glenda   sp
also wanted a good grade for another
reason˄if she did well, her parents   r-s
would let her spend a week with her
friend at a vacation cabin. She took
a deep breath to calm her nerves. She reached out a   sp
steady hand and open˄*ed*   v-t
the class room door. She saw her friend
across the room. Glenda took a seat

near her. When the teacher, Mrs. Montagu, called for

silence and passed out the

tests, Glenda relaxed. She had studied,   frag

and she knew the material.

The final exam was at noon. Glenda felt her hands sweating, her head aching, and her heart pounding. This test was very important. Her score on this one exam would affect her grade. She wanted at least a B to keep up her average. Glenda also wanted a good grade for another reason; if she did well, her parents would let her spend a week with her friend at a vacation cabin. She took a deep breath to calm her nerves. She reached out a steady hand and opened the classroom door. She saw her friend across the room. Glenda took a seat near her. When the teacher, Mrs. Montagu, called for silence and passed out the tests, Glenda relaxed. She had studied, and she knew the material.

Posttest

1. a
2. a
3. b
4. b
5. Bree, Lauren, and Rachel saw the new movie last weekend.
6. Donna had the flu all week!
7. Mrs. McCann's class read *Huckleberry Finn* this year.
8. Bree, Lauren, and Rachel saw the new movie last weekend.
9. Donna had the flu all week!
10. Mrs. McCann's class read *Huckleberry Finn* this year.
11. a
12. b
13. c
14. a
15. Answers will vary. The following is a sample answer: As I was running the hundred-yard-dash, my nose was red with cold.
16. Answers will vary. The following is a sample answer: I saw that woman with the red skirt at the museum.
17. Answers will vary. The following is a sample answer: Nina has to study for a test; she also has to do her math homework.
18. Reading, swimming, and baking are some of Neil's favorite activities.
19. a
20. b
21. c

22. b
23. a
24. There are seven errors. Some corrections may vary. The following are sample answers:

Margo's plan worked with out a hitch.

Yelena would never guess that her
                 surprise
friends were planning a (surprize) party   sp
    since
for her, her birthday was not for   c-s

three weeks. Last week, Margo and

erik called Yelena's sister to find out

whom to invite. Then they bought
                 ed
invitations, filled them out, stamp

them, and put them in the mail.
        has
Everyone ~~have~~ agreed to come.   s-v agr

Now Erik just has to get Yelena to

Margos house. He told the birthday girl that Margo needs

help studying.

25. Margo's plan worked without a hitch. Yelena would never guess that her friends were planning a surprise party for her, since her birthday was not for three weeks. Last week, Margo and Erik called Yelena's sister to find out whom to invite. Then they bought invitations, filled them out, stamped them, and put them in the mail. Everyone has agreed to come. Now Erik just has to get Yelena to Margo's house. He told the birthday girl that Margo needs help studying.

Student Record-Keeping Form

Student Name	Student ID	Class Period	Pretest Score	Unit___ Score	Unit___ Score	Unit___ Score	Unit___ Score	Unit___ Score	Unit___ Score	Unit___ Score	Unit___ Score
1.											
2.											
3.											
4.											
5.											
6.											
7.											
8.											
9.											
10.											
11.											
12.											
13.											
14.											
15.											
16.											
17.											
18.											
19.											
20.											
21.											
22.											
23.											
24.											
25.											
26.											
27.											
28.											
29.											
30.											

Proofreaders' Marks

Symbol	Type of error	Example
ℛ	delete	It is in ~~at~~ the atmosphere.
◡	close up; write as one word	It is in the atmo◯sphere.
∧	insert	It is in ∧atmosphere. _the_
/	insert space	It is in the/atmosphere.
stet	let marked text stand as is	It is in ~~the atmosphere.~~ _stet_
∿	transpose (change places)	It in͡is the atmosphere.

Symbol		Type of error	Example
in margin	**in text**		
sp	⬭	spelling error	It is in the (atmusphear.)
p		punctuation error:	
	⋏	insert comma	He lives in Chicago⋏Illinois.
	⋁	insert apostrophe	It⋁s in the atmosphere.
	⊙	insert period	It is in the atmosphere⊙
	⋏	insert semicolon	I am here⋏you are there.
	⋏	insert colon	Dear Mr. Shawmut⋏
	⋁	insert quotation marks	He said,⋁Go home.
	( )	put in parentheses	This is sodium(Na).
cap	≡	capitalize word(s)	He lives in chicago.
lc	/	write in lower case	It is in the /Atmosphere.

Proofreaders' Marks, *continued*

Symbol	Type of error	Example
s-v agr	subject-verb agreement	**One** of the students are here. *is*
ref	pronoun reference error	Every**one** is responsible for their own car. *his or her*
vt	error in verb tense	I **told** him I am going home. *was*

Symbol	Type of error	Example
ss	error in sentence structure	I cannot in the morning see that customer.
frag	sentence fragment (not a complete sentence)	Because I like to eat.
r-s	run-on sentence (too many thoughts without proper punctuation)	I cannot go to the store because my mother wants me to scrub the floor she always has me doing something when I want to go somewhere.
c-s	comma splice (two complete sentences joined only by a comma)	I signed up for a Spanish class, my best friend wants to learn Russian.
awk	awkward sentence structure, such as dangling modifier	**Walking** to the store, a car pulled out right in front of me.
||	parallelism mistake	He had finally decided on his blue jacket and **what** tie he would wear.

Introduction to Composition Test Pack

Strategies for Standardized Testing

Test-taking is a skill. Just as you learn rules of grammar, you can learn to succeed on standardized tests. State standardized tests are intended to measure your understanding of state and national curriculum standards. Of course, the best preparation for these exams is attention and participation in your daily classroom lessons.

Tests will vary in their structure and content. Some tests will contain multiple-choice questions with four answers, some with five. You might be required to write a long essay, or a series of short answers, or both. Whatever the structure of your specific exam, there are some general strategies you can use in order to test your best.

Know the Test

One of the most important things you can do to prepare for a test is to become familiar with it in advance. If your teacher has sample tests or questions, these are the best resources for you to use for practice. You will feel more confident on test day if you are already familiar with the directions. If you open your test booklet to see a set of directions you've worked with before, you won't have to spend valuable test time learning them.

Knowing the exam will also prepare you for the way particular standards are tested. For example, some exams will ask you to identify a grammatical error in a sentence, while others will ask you to choose the correct version. Make sure there are as few surprises as possible on test day by knowing in advance what types of question to expect.

It's Your Test

Once you sit down with the test booklet, it's your test. You decide your approach to individual questions. Some people, for example, would rather solve a problem before looking at the answer choices. Others like to scan the choices before attempting a solution. Whichever approach makes you feel more comfortable and confident is the right approach for you.

The challenge on these exams is not just answering the questions, but answering them in the allotted time. It's important to pace yourself so that you have time to finish each section and preferably have some time left to check your work. Generally, you are allotted a specific amount of time for each particular section. Within each section, the order in which you approach the questions is up to you. If you encounter an item that gives you trouble, you can skip it and return to it later. Circle these questions in your test booklet so that you can quickly and easily find them. If you do skip questions or move around in a section, be extra careful that you're filling in your answers next to the right question numbers on your answer sheet.

Strategies for Standardized Testing, *cont.*

On most tests, you're free to mark up your test booklet. In addition to circling questions you skip, you might want to mark questions you're unsure about. Those can be the first questions you revisit if you have any time left at the end of a section. You can also underline important information in reading passages, cross out answer choices you've eliminated, and so forth.

Making Choices

If your exam doesn't deduct points for wrong answers, it's a good idea to fill in an answer for every question. Even if there is a wrong answer penalty, making an educated guess can improve your score. Many questions on state standardized exams are in multiple-choice format. You might understand enough about a question to eliminate one or more of its answer choices. If so, you dramatically increase your odds of selecting the correct answer from the remaining choices. For example, you might be able to cross off a vocabulary word that you know doesn't fit the bill.

It is always important to read each question carefully to make sure you're doing exactly what it asks. Not every multiple-choice question asks you to choose the one correct response. In other words, you might be asked to select the one incorrect choice or to decide whether all of the choices are correct.

Some key words to look out for in multiple-choice questions are:

- sometimes/always/never
- except
- all of the above
- synonym/antonym
- same/opposite

The foundation for success on your test is the content you learn in your classroom. Using some basic strategies and doing practice tests will also help you get ready for test time. Follow the formula for success below, and you can be confident that you'll do your best on test day.

classroom knowledge + strategic insight + practice = SUCCESS

Strategies for Standardized Testing, *cont.*

Here are some additional hints to help you succeed on any standardized test.

Helpful Hints

1. Listen carefully to all instructions from the person giving the test.

2. Read directions carefully. Be sure you understand all the directions before beginning that section of the test.

3. Read each question carefully. Then read all the answer choices before you answer the question.

4. If it's taking you a lot of time to answer one question, move on to the next one. If you take too much time on one question, you may not have a chance to get through the whole test. Answer the questions you know first. Then go back to the others if you have time.

5. Be sure to mark your answers on the answer sheet that comes with the test booklet. You will probably be asked to shade the circle that contains the letter of your answer.

6. Take care when marking your answer sheet. Check to make sure that the number on the answer sheet matches the number of the question you are answering.

7. Since most standardized tests are scored by a machine, mark your answer clearly and darkly. Make sure you mark only one answer for each question.

8. If you have time, go back and check your answers.